GUINDON

TOGETHER AGAIN

GUINDON

TOGETHER AGAIN

by Richard Guindon

Andrews, McMeel & Parker
A Universal Press Syndicate Affiliate
Kansas City ● New York

ISBN: 0-8362-2075-7

Library of Congress Catalog Card Number: 85-73417

Water wings — another way that white bread is better than whole wheat.

Comedy archeology

Since only the wealthy can afford homes overlooking the ocean, do you realize that if America is attacked on either coast our first line of defense would be the rich?

"I once dated a dude who was so good-looking that I thought he was a manufacturer's rep for God."

Motels seem to have worked out just how few towels it takes to cause an argument.

Carp were once used as breathalyzers. The police figured any fool who would put a carp in his mouth and blow into it would have to be drunk.

Sumerian pot unearthed with a cute
set of Sumerian potholders.

"Wait! I think we're supposed to get drunk first."

"Yes, I have a question for Dr. Ruth."

"Ed, could you come in here? I'm caught on the refrigerator magnets!"

"I love that look, but I could never pull it off."

"Do you realize that we are the only interesting people we know?"

"Naughty robot! Naughty, naughty robot!"

The Internal Revenue Service has ruled that you need not include gift carp on your return.

Are we going to get some legislation that will allow us to eat out on our birthday without being molested by restaurant help?

"Super shag. It's not for everybody."

I'm not looking forward to the future because I think we'll have to dress something like this.

"FARGO!" The soon-to-be-released TV series about the brawling, ambitious Ferguson clan who made their fortune selling paintings on velvet.

"I do exist! I do! I do!"

Before you buy a Euro-carp, be warned that the large ones don't fit in trash compactors.

One of the reasons why, in the game of life, it is so difficult to keep your eye on the ball.

"We don't think of him as a pet. He's more like one of the family."

"Your car won't be ready until Tuesday. The computer is down."

Marvin Fenster, still trying to wear out his platform shoes so he can get on with his next "look."

Refuse hunting with carp

"I'm the morning person in our family. Harry's more a night person."

The misuse of okra is responsible for more food-related injuries than all other vegetables together.

YOUNG PLUMBERS IN LOVE.

The state of California has a hot line for stolen grocery carts. The maximum sentence is 30 days and a $500 fine.

"My Harvey, like most Americans, lives in terror of not being hip."

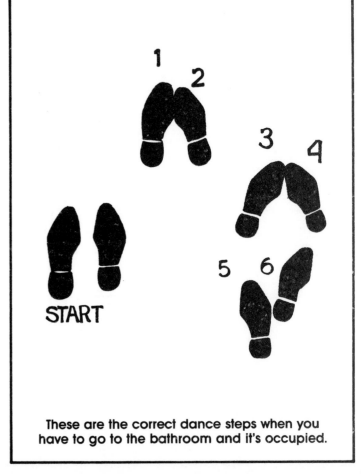

These are the correct dance steps when you have to go to the bathroom and it's occupied.

"Bea doesn't like to hear any criticism of Reagan because he's such a hunk."

"Of course you know that this means that I, too, will get a power blower."

A federally protected witness testifying before a Senate committee on corruption in the cartooning industry.

"I understand that in some areas of the country the cauliflower is considered not merely decorative."

Along with their other rights, when are women going to demand full-size watches?

Seated from left to right: 1. Hugo J. Filmore

"I'm just feeding Ralph. I forgot to get dog food."

"Did you decide to rent that apartment across from the high-rise?"

Corrective clothing

WE HAVE TIME FOR ONE MORE QUESTION

"If you get to 1936, stop and pick up a cheap chicken and a nice roast."

"They've heard the buzzer, and now she's running around kicking dirty clothes under the furniture and he's putting a shirt on . . ."

"Go out there with your head held high, put your face to the sun, and try not to bump into anything."

Walking into rooms and forgetting why.

DID YOU CLEAN UP YOUR ROOM YET?

ALMOST

Another thing teenagers do just to bug us.

The movie *Flashdance* has certainly given hope to a lot of steelworkers in a troubled industry.

The Suzuki method of humming

"Besides their other contributions to our society, lawyers could be an important source of protein."

What if the moon blabbed to the sun about what it sees at night?

Bah House

"He was released on his own recognizance. We're all out
on our own recognizance, aren't we?"

The arrival of okra on American shores is undocumented,
but it probably looked something like this.

"Wait a minute! Where are you taking me? This isn't the way to the bingo hall!"

"Push the door open enough to turn the light on."

Although we don't wish him any bad luck, a lot of us hope Roger Frud is not our next singing idol. We can't afford to have his "look" catch on.

"Myron, I asked you to acquire some tax shelters!"

The Jif peanut butter-Pepsi Cola-Blatz beer taste test

Get a pencil and paper ready if you want Eunice Benson's method of disguising leftover meat loaf.

So far, business card-related injuries are confined to very, very beautiful women in singles bars.

Eunice Benson, with her illegally recorded videotape of "The Benny Hill Show," making her break for it.

Still nothing for Bea Fenster from Burt Reynolds on her offer to be a surrogate mother for his child.

. . . and then one day cable TV came to sleepy little Bensonville, and no one was ever, ever seen again.

TV DINNERS

VIDEO TAPE DINNERS

People I can't play trivia with

With private companies going into the pay phone business,
I'm hoping for some phones with new, fun themes.

"True, we used to butt heads to establish territory, but today we do it with zoning."

"It's a 14-day book. Are you ready to make that kind of commitment?"

"Do you remember the first time you threw up?"

The Bad Suit Convention has just been asked by the hotel management not to hang around the lobby.

"One thing I like about Orvis — he's easy to buy for."

"Tom, no! You're a tomato and he can stir, mix, chop, blend, whip, and purée."

"There is such a thing as good stress, but I don't think this is it, dear."

The proliferation of cloth ropes in our culture has finally gotten to Eunice Benson.

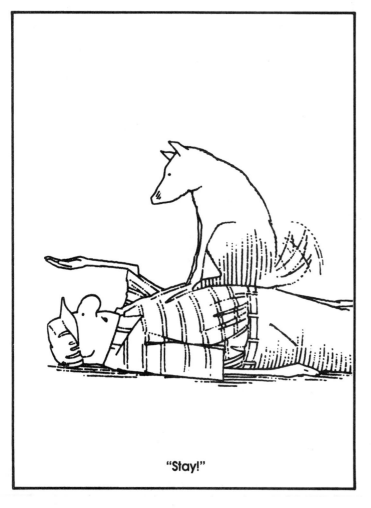

"Stay!"

Wait long enough and fashion becomes satire.

Stunt carp

"Cow's gone crazy. She believes they're going to kill and eat everybody but the dog."

Carp are the poor man's carp.

One way to visualize what $6.95 per square foot might look like.

Bug repellent on strips of cloth fastened around your ankles should keep insects out of your food.

"I used to think I was ethically superior to used car salesmen until I sold my old car."

Sooner or later we're all going to have to toss some of our junk.

"I got most of them from my first husband. He was a famous cat burglar."

The Associated Press, North Dakota
bureau, artist's conception

It can be quite a shock meeting the wives and
husbands of the people you work with. Best keep
the dispensary open during the company party.

THE MÖBIUS STRIP HAS NO
BEGINNING OR END.

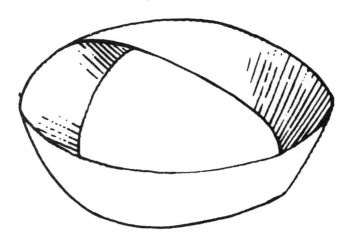

AN IMPROVED MÖBIUS STRIP
WITH AN OFF RAMP.

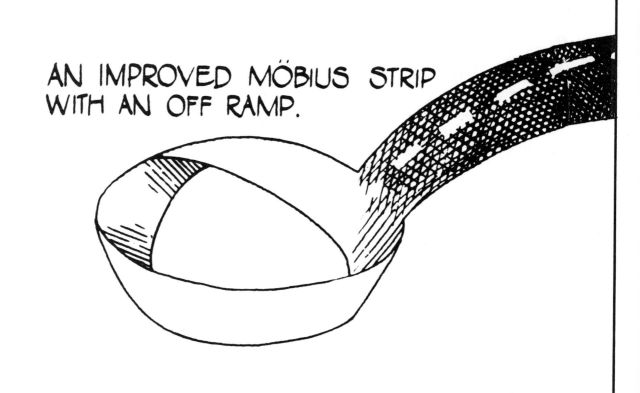

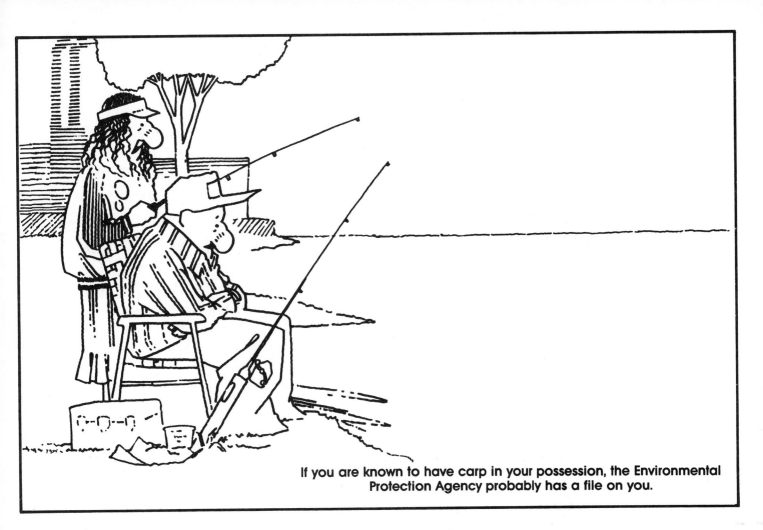

If you are known to have carp in your possession, the Environmental Protection Agency probably has a file on you.

Volunteerism at its very, very worst

The Foss family, here, is so neat that when they bought a model home, they left the sign up.

"He looked just like a government witness."

A hold-up, using a lawyer

"Now your package includes the complimentary beef jerky or a free bowling ball wash. Your choice!"

"I think there are two N's in Cezanne."

DOS AND DON'TS IN JAPAN...

Don't muss the hair of a Japanese you've just been introduced to, as they are, for the most part, a fairly neat people.

"Times are really hard when you can get people to run 26 miles for a $6.00 T-shirt."

If you talk to yourself, it's a good idea to carry a plant.

"If anything should happen to me, honey, would you carry on my work?"

"Goodness! Don't you ever do that to me again!"

What your cat thinks you're doing when you're out buying cat food.

Things teenagers do just to bug us

"You're endangering your lake privileges, Fenster."

Hester Foster hasn't turned on the radio ever since she discovered herbicides can be broadcast.

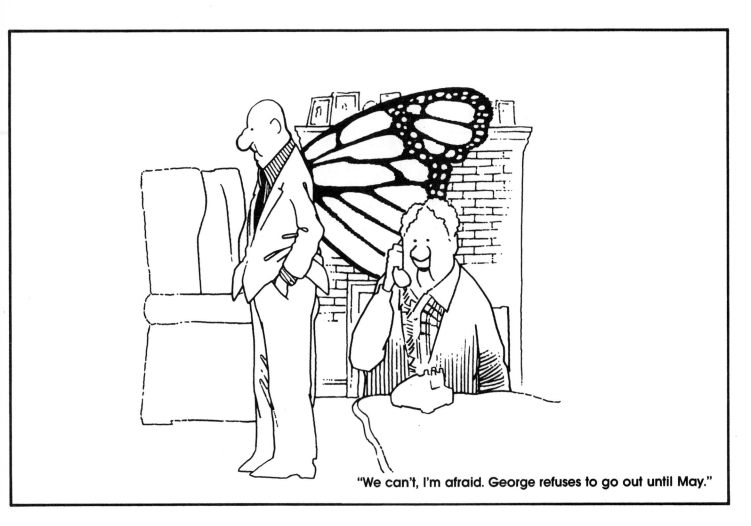

"We can't, I'm afraid. George refuses to go out until May."

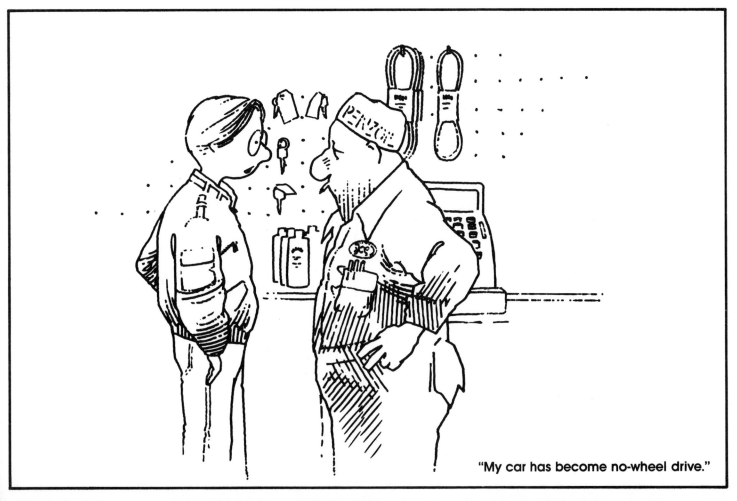

"My car has become no-wheel drive."

America's greatest swindler of vegetables was a man named Reginald Foster. At the time of his arrest, police found him trying to skip out of Toledo with three suitcases of wax beans.

"Does the doctor know how to DO medicine, or does he just have a practice?"

"First of all, let me assure you that this low price is not the result of a government sting operation."

"The carts won't come apart. Is this the mating season?"

It's 3 p.m. and the Fensters are still at a stand-off about who is going to get up first and make coffee.

"Hi! It's me, your checking account, and we really need to talk."

Harvey has had to give up on self-hypnosis because he keeps
making a fool of himself doing imitations of barnyard animals.

Sadly, the addiction usually starts harmlessly enough with someone finding a piece of plastic air-bubble packaging and popping the bubbles, one by one. But some people go on to buy the stuff in bulk.

"Can't you read?"

"Would you go out with me sometime? I need the adrenaline rush."

"The only other person I saw going 55 looked
like he had drugs in his car."

New Wave western

A. Harvey Foster in his loudest outfit
B. Harvey Foster's sound barrier

GARRY MOORE DODY GOODMAN DICK CAVET

In case you wondered where they put the people
who are no longer seen on TV.

"Try wrapping half an onion in Reynolds Wrap and the other half in another leading plastic. Set the timer for five minutes. You'll notice that Reynolds Wrap clings better." — TV commercial.

"There goes the 7:10 Carp. It must be around 11:00."

"Would you like us to tell you midway through the meal if everything is okay?"

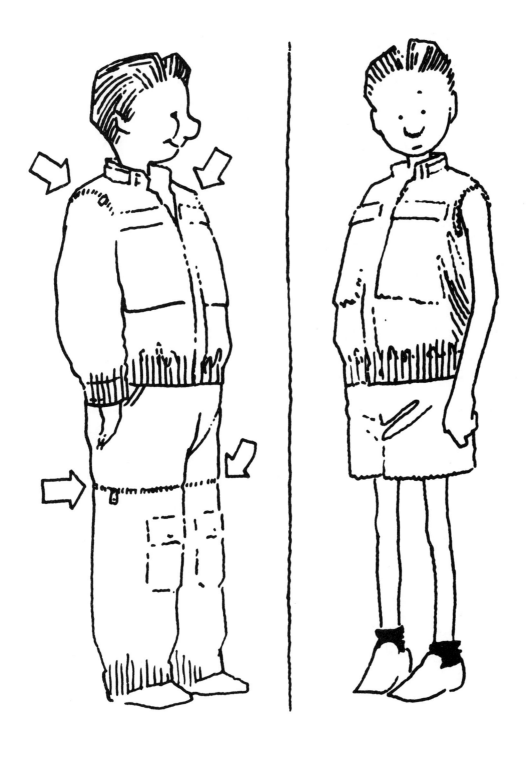

You can detach the sleeves and legs of some men's
clothing in case you want to look strange quick.

"Ten minutes into the credits Flo yells, 'To hell with the grips,' and the audience joined in."

"Used to be we had to play records backward to hear the sleazy stuff."

"I'm ignoring you."

"I'm not your waitress. Your waitress is an overweight bimbo with large pores."

A ball with improved rollability

"I'm not moving an inch until you put on your belt."

A lot of us dread the day when cordless phones get
a long enough range to go anywhere.

"Today I'm only talking to every fourth caller, like disc jockeys do."

Historian   Hysterian

"Hey, fella! You want to get in on these three-for-a-dollar onions?"

"Today's vegetable is beets, the soup is split pea, and I am the catch of the day."

"We're not selling. We just felt like meeting some new people."

"I think that first we get famous, then we have a battle with drugs and alcohol."

Participatory cartooning

We might be sorry when we finally understand dolphin talk.

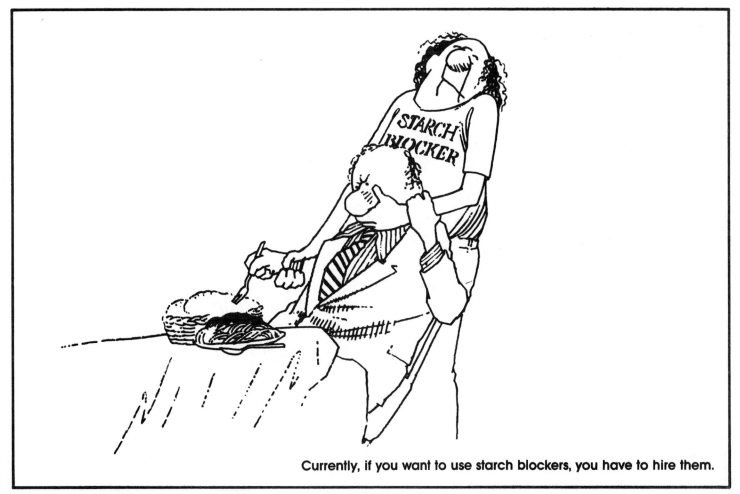

Currently, if you want to use starch blockers, you have to hire them.

"You should be grateful. How often do you find a waitress
who knows something about nutrition?"

Sure, you can make big money stuffing envelopes at home,
but they don't tell you what goes in them.

Polyester waste dumps will last as long as the pyramids.
I hope the discount stores are happy.

"Here's your favorite, dear,
geometrically shaped meat."

Young Frankenstein's first creation was so bizarre that he threw it in a nearby river.

That fool Henry Fenster, still waiting for the 15 minutes of fame Andy Warhol promised everyone.

"I've made so many mistakes that I now think of my life as pure research."

One can understand running in a marathon, but who are those people watching the whole thing?

It's Marvin's very favorite jacket. If only he could convince people to stop taking swatches from it . . . .

The Bensons are ready for their trip to Eunice's cousin in Arizona.
They have to be at the airport in nine hours.

"You can smoke carp, but never, never inhale."

1) Lock the door. 2) Take the phone off the hook after you've called into work sick. 3) Turn on a soap. To veg out takes planning and discipline.

"Hi! I'm Marvin, and I'll be your car wash attendant."

"It's not just a carp. It's a designer carp."

"It's good, lightweight reading. The kind of stuff John and Bo Derek might have around the house."

"They told me that you can use the container to keep dentures in."

"Darn! I keep doing that."

The Bensons have spent the summer on their boat. Next year it goes into the water.

"How come Doans Pills know where your backache is? Don't they ever go to your foot and just fool around?"

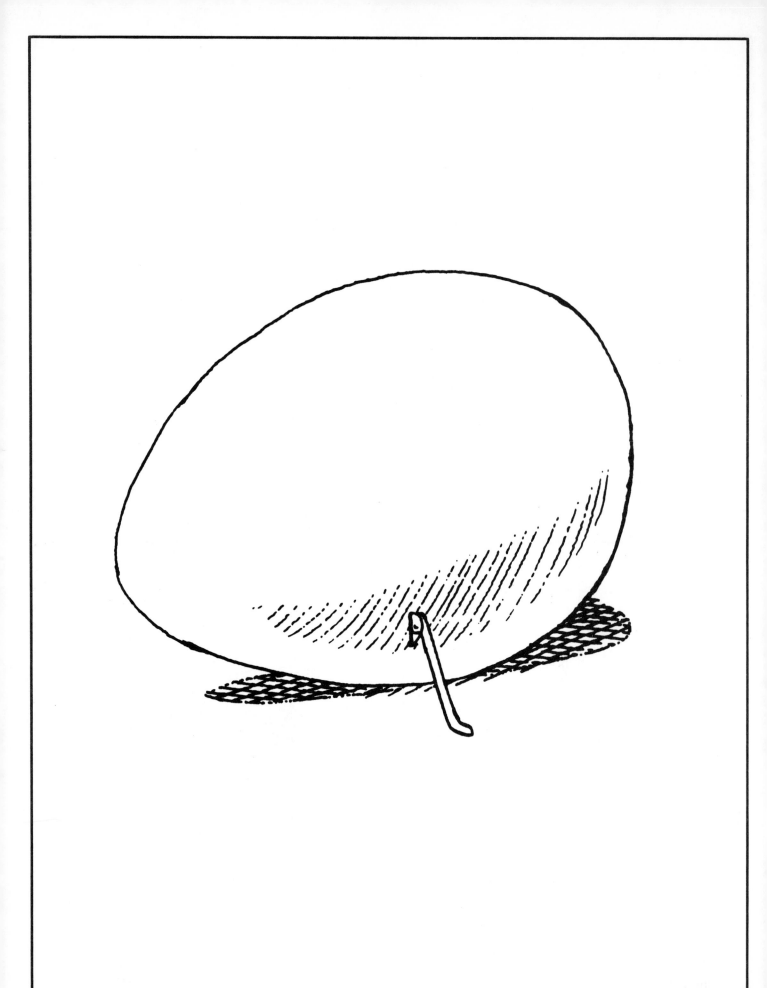

An improved egg with a kickstand

"I DID want to lose six inches. But not in height, jerk!"

Those mail-order brides can give you quite a start.

"Have you seen this man? We're looking all over for him."

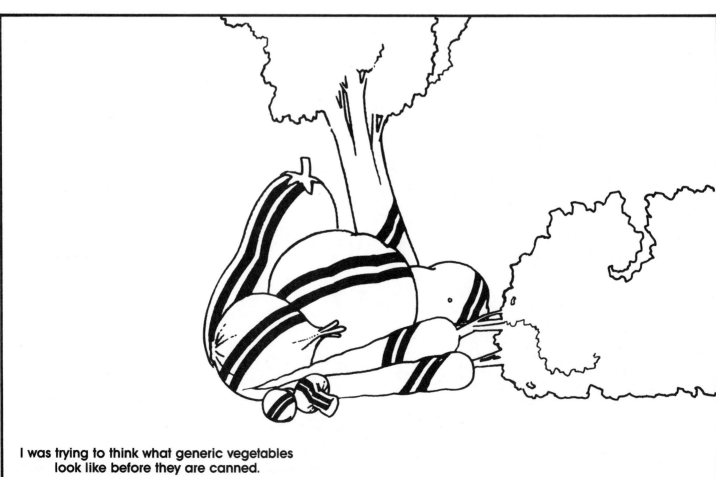

I was trying to think what generic vegetables
look like before they are canned.

Why do people get so heated over the subject of "Youth in Asia"? The kids never hurt anybody.

"Let's go hang around the blood pressure machine at the airport and pick up some dudes."

Halley's comment

"Before I give you my check, do you have any identification?"

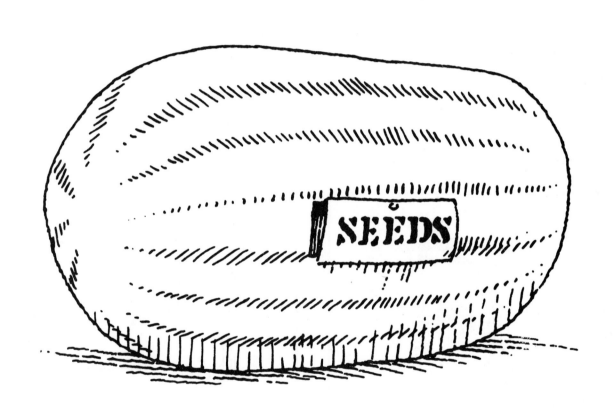

An improved watermelon

Paris in the '30s...
We had drunk far too much
pernod, Ernest, F. Scott and I.
.....Even Jane Austen was
drunk.

A DOCU-MEMOIR.

It's a good idea from time to time to leave
yourself open to new experiences.

EARLY AMERICAN

THE "DUKE"

Let's hope that the people who make home
computers will soon come out with some designs
that we can live with.

OPEN UP! WE'VE GOT MIXED FRUIT FOR YOU.

Miami Virtue

"You should never eat more than four carp a month,
or one box of lawn and garden bags."

"I need one tsp. of garlic, two egg whites, one tsp. shallots . . ."

In just a moment, the motel maid is going to discover that
Harvey shined his shoes with the bedspread.

"It's Roger Fenster, the person."

A state-of-the-art chocolate chip cookie

"Every time you leave, Margo, a big part of me goes with you."

Give a man a fish and he can eat
for a day. Teach a man to fish . . .

Is this a national franchise, or are people just winging it?

One way to celebrate turning 30 is to camp out in your parents' backyard.

"When the going gets tough, the tough probably put cigarettes out on their knuckles."

"Who keeps putting these under 'K'?"

James Bennett opens the summer games . . .

"I'm not here to see anyone, thank you. Waiting is my hobby."

Let's hope that those talking electronics, found in the dashboards of cars, don't find their way into the rest of our lives.

Call forwarding

"I didn't know International Harvester made farm equipment. I thought they just made hats."

"Ask your father, dear. He's parenting today."

"You have a lunch with 'Real People' Tuesday, David Letterman will call you on the air Wednesday, and you got Charles Kuralt Thursday."

"I'm sorry, but the other owners of Members Only jackets want to buy your jacket back."

"That's why I sometimes appear to be heavy-set."

"The back seat of my car has been declared a landfill."

"'Aries: A new romance enters your life today.' You're staying home from work, Aries."

"Harvey likes the music on the exercise shows. It really gets his foot tapping."

An improved cube (right), half the size of ordinary cubes. It has a convenient carrying handle.

A dog that's good with kids

Probably the reason why wallets made from carp never caught on.

Fortunately, most of the Ninji have found meaningful, alternative work.

"I distinctly said in the ad 'Serious Buyers Only.'"

Sometimes getting the USDA to grade a carp can be quite a chore.

THIS YEAR, OUR JR. ACHIEVEMENT PROJECT WISHES TO ANNOUNCE A TAKEOVER BID ON 4H.

WOULD YOU ORDER FOR ME? I'M INVISIBLE.

"Remind me at 3 o'clock to rotate my tube socks a half turn. It saves the heels."

"Who's next?"

"Just hold everything! This woman has been to Frederick's of North Dakota!"

"You would have to eat this much carp to equal the vitamins and minerals in just one bowl of Total."

MODERATION IN ALL THINGS.

(Including moderation)

"I won't go out with you, Rodney, because you're too rich and thin."

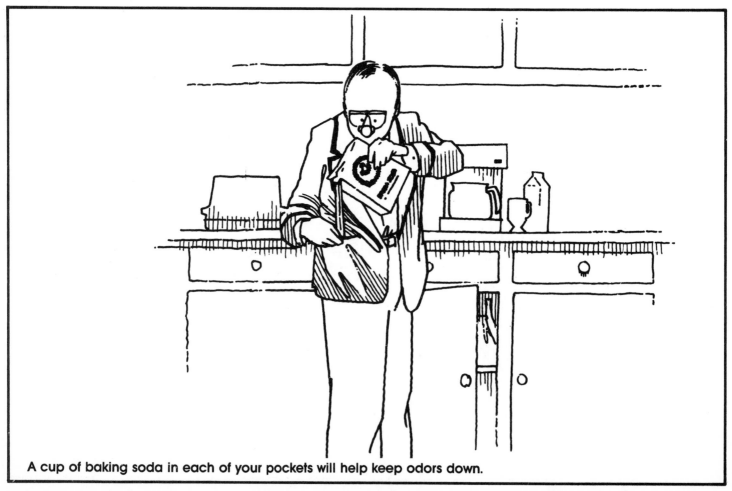

A cup of baking soda in each of your pockets will help keep odors down.

Beware of mail fraud, especially during the coming holiday season. Flo Hester is out $32 and still doesn't have any nudes of Wayne Newton.

"You need to get out, dear."

Be sure to have a physical before jumping on the current
fad of opening blister packs to disco music.

"If I forget anyone's name, you Nancy-Reagan me."

"I don't trust natural. People die all the
time from natural causes."

"You never outgrow your need for plaid."

"I've canceled your subscription to *National Geographic*, Rodney."

"Just who are these rich people with the new cars who get to park inside the airport terminal?"

"One of us is going to have to tell your aunt that the toaster refuses to wear it."

"Harry's not against jogging. He's just unable to conquer his fear of shin splints."

PLAYING HOCKEY.

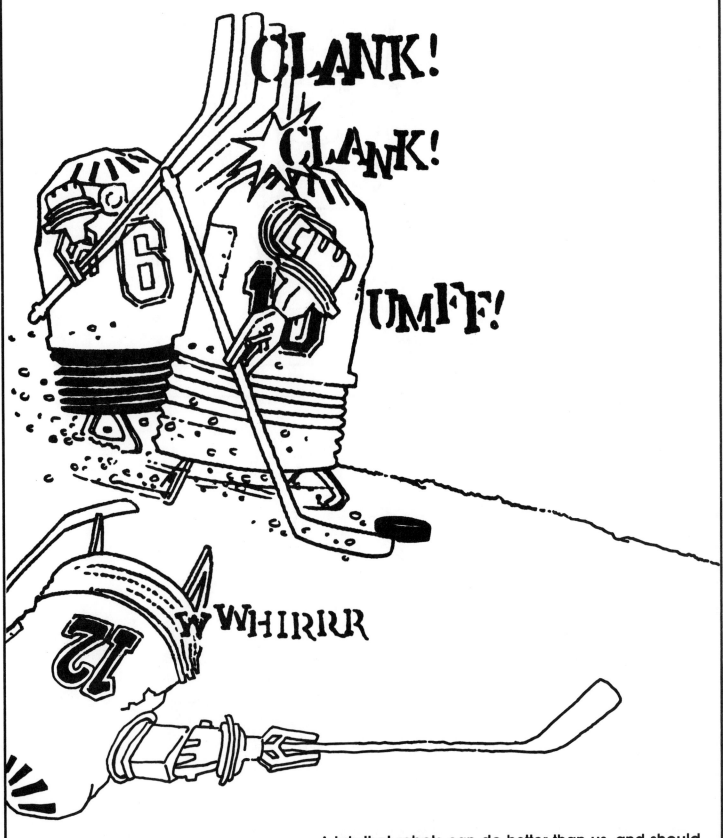

A job that robots can do better than us, and should.

"Excuse the condition of the place, but I live here."

Eunice Benson played her videotape of *The Sound of Music* again last night. She's sending a couple of bucks to the author.

It has just occurred to Flo Benson that she hasn't been in street clothes for five years.

Before chickens became domesticated, they'd migrate south. I'm guessing, but, it must have looked something like this.

"I can't bowl in my jogging shoes, and I can't play paddleball in my softball shoes. I can walk in, but not jog in, my tennis . . ."

"I have a bomb, and unless you give me $4.00, I'm going to show it."

IF YOU'VE DECIDED NOT TO ACCEPT THIS OFFER, PLEASE READ THIS...

WE KNOW WHERE YOU LIVE.

Some of us who weren't invited to the Diet Coke Gala dressed up to watch it at home.

"I know where the better dresses are. Where are your better people?"

"We only go around once, so let's get all the rest we can."

"Harry, let's not get serious with each other, because
I don't think of you, you know, that way."

"My hobby is house-hunting, because I like the part where the real estate people ask me about my needs."

WRRRRRRRRRrrrrrrro

The Moped Patrol

Mrs. Benson still refusing to use the mails until the
Post Office has a sale on stamps.

WRONG

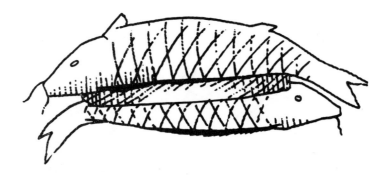

RIGHT

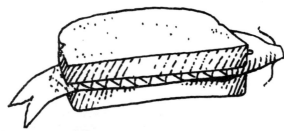

In making a carp sandwich, never never put the
carp on the outside of the bread.

"Does our mystery guest have his own paper route?"

"If they had house arrest in this country, I think our house would be among the first to get arrested."

Because he's always been told not to go into the water after eating, Harry Feldman has never actually been in the water.

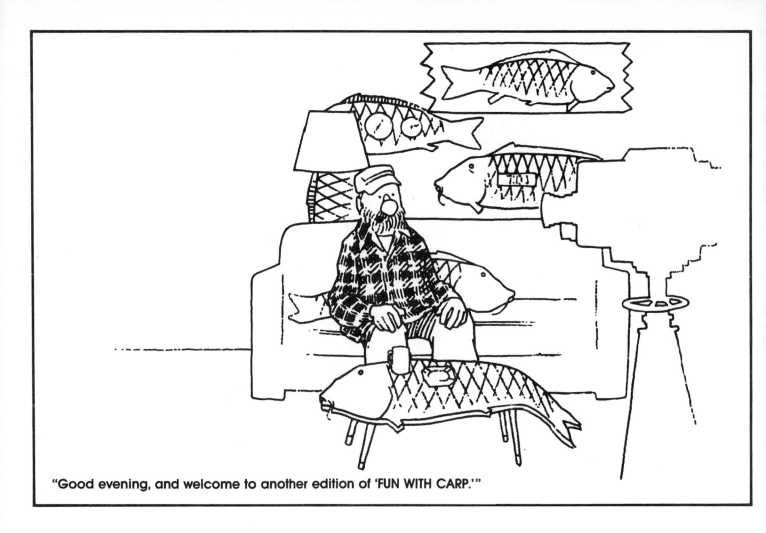

"Good evening, and welcome to another edition of 'FUN WITH CARP.'"

The ceremony to renew the membership and subscription to the *National Geographic* is no small matter at the Foster household.

"My nephew's got a good job when he graduates. The kind where you don't have to wear a hat."

"Young man, you have to stop letting clothing
salesmen make a fool out of you."

"How come it never occurs to a dog
to scratch our ears in return?"

"Is Elsie the cow denying her own
kid milk so I can have it?"

Harry has a height problem. According to the
weight chart he should be seven feet tall.

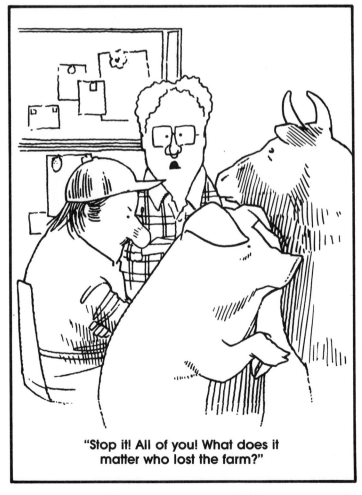

"Stop it! All of you! What does it
matter who lost the farm?"

Carp returning from Newark with souvenirs

"As soon as you see the first eight, ten dead carp,
you know that spring is on its way."

"Come to think of it, even though it's traditionally men's work,
it doesn't entail any heavy lifting."

"When I first met you, I thought you were really going to be somebody. Instead, you're you."

"When we started this commune back in '68, I never thought the day would come when we'd have to consider a dress code."

"Harry had a rash very similar to the pattern in your rug."

"Why can't they dress up those ugly TV dish antennas with some Norman Rockwell, or the Melmac wheat pattern?"

During fishing season, it's a good idea to post a list of baits that may not be kept in the fridge.

"It started with a plastic slipcover for the couch."

"I'll tell you what life is. It's all the junk that's happened to you so far."

"Did you know that of all the animals on earth, man is the most dangerous?"

A lot of us just can't wait until we get video polka music.

"It's from *Time* magazine and it says 'IMPORTANT! OPEN IMMEDIATELY!' You'd better come home from work."

Garnish will help a great deal in the preparation of carp, as soon as the chefs work out the details.

"It happens to all of us sooner or later, honey. Boy, I sure remember my disappointment in seeing my first disc jockey."

Bob, Harry, and Barry showing their breathtaking ensembles
that say, "I am the total bowler."

Make-ahead gifts for Christmas — the handkerchief cap.

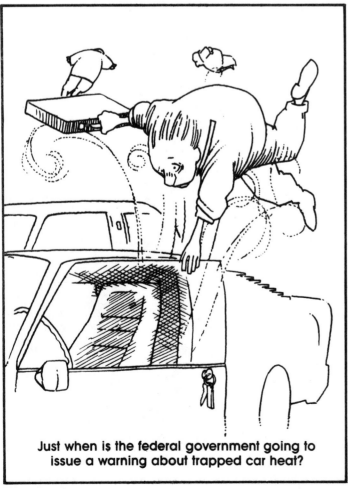

Just when is the federal government going to issue a warning about trapped car heat?

Next week, Harvey Foster gets the suit he's put on layaway. Both he and his family are looking forward to it.

"Is there such a thing as a digital watch
that just tells time?"

"Deep down inside, I still haven't granted
Alaska and Hawaii statehood."

A prediction: In the year 2074, A.D., a curator at
the Museum of Modern Art in New York will
conclude that the happy face and Pac-Man were
done by the same artist.

"Now, how much would you be willing to pay for
all this — $39.95? $29.95? But wait! What if I threw
in this screwdriver kit?"

The Carp Song... ♩
CARP IS SINGULAR ♫
CARP ARE PLURAL ♪
♪ CARP ARE CITY
CARP IS RURAL... ♪
♪
...SOMETHING
SOMETHING...

Let me get back to you on this . . .

Travel tip for businessmen in Japan: Don't put your wingtips up on those little tables because I think they eat off them.

"Oh, nothing much. Bob and I got cabin fever."

"Your wife, Eunice, is famous for her cheese and macaroni casserole. Is it difficult for you, as a man, to live in her shadow?"

Another meeting of the Carp Advisory Board still without anyone to advise.

"Do you have a novel where the characters are essentially Hummel figures?"

If you think about it, mannequins are to merchants what decoys are to duck hunters.

Today Eunice is 60. She has her eyes closed, watching the speedometer in her mind turn over the zeros.

"I don't have a business card, but I've had this brochure printed about myself which touches on the highlights of my life."

"The ad was not a misprint. We ARE throwing in a turbot with every new car purchase. You won't find a better eating fish anywhere."

Count your blessings that "The A Team" caught on, and
that the network didn't have to use its replacement.

For the at-home game of "Meeting of the Minds," Darrell will play Caesar, Darrell, Jr., is Napoleon, and Maude is Cher.

Weekends, you can have an industrial park all to yourself. That's why they're called parks.

"Yah! Yah! The animals lost! People own the planet."

"If you do become a juggler, dear, where do they work?"

Vicki, the chimp, using language cards, is telling a researcher that she is an existentialist. But in reality she is a logical positivist.

"Boy, you should have seen some of the junk people bought at our garage sale."

"Those are called bras, but I think it's to keep the car from throwing up."

It's not for everybody, this business of ordering different dishes of Chinese food and sharing it.

It's permissible for singles who don't cook to allow their guests to eat directly from the refrigerator.

For people who don't qualify for Club Med

"I should have never gotten into carp futures. Carp don't have no futures."

"Take the bench, too. He would have wanted you to have it."

Myron Fenster fought a carp in his boat for 45 minutes before he could dispatch it. Uninjured, he was covered from head to toe with hickeys.

"Want to split a Manwich? I can't eat a whole one."

"Maybe you could try the other diet where you eat just the one big meal."

"I wanted to major in astrology but I'm no good at science."

"You want to trade your marmalade for a concord grape jelly?"

"*People* magazine wouldn't promise, but they will send a photographer if they possibly can."

"Dad grounded me because I beat him out of this job."

"Oh, that. It's just an old purse of your father's, dear."

Low tech